GRANNY GADGET

Michaela Morgan
Illustrated by Sarah Horne

Granny Gadget loved to make machines.

"This is my machine to do the housework," she said.

"I've got to make a new machine today," said
Granny Gadget to her cat.

"I've looked high and low, and near and far.
I can't find your little kitten anywhere."

3

So she made a machine for finding lost pets.

The machine had big ears – to listen for pets.

It had a big nose – to sniff out pets.

It had long legs – to run after pets.

It had long arms – to reach out and grab pets.

"Let's start it!" said Ellie.

Ben counted, "Five, four, three, two, one, GO!"

And off it went.

It ran round the house, upstairs and downstairs.
It found lost socks, lost sweets, lost toys, and
lots of things that were not lost at all.
    But it didn't find the kitten.

"Oh, no," said Granny Gadget. "What a mess!
And I still haven't found the kitten."
   She went off to have a rest.

Ben and Ellie got out Granny's housework machine. They read the instructions.

"Pull string number one," read Ellie.

Ben pulled the string. The machine started to hum.

"Push button number two," read Ellie.

Ben did that, too. The machine grew and grew.

When they pulled string number three, it buzzed like a bee.

When they pulled string number four,
the machine started to roar.
But when they pulled string number five,
it really came alive!

9

It jumped up and down
and spun round and round.
It washed the floor and
dried the dishes.

It dusted the books
and cooked the dinner.

It fed the cat and
walked the dog.

But . . .
it got hotter and hotter
and hotter.
  It began to fizz and pop.

Then it washed the dog and dusted the dinner.
It cooked the books and fed the floor.

It ran into the garden and washed the trees.
It dusted the flowers, it dried the shed.

"Stop! Stop!" shouted the children.
Granny came running.
"Stop! Stop!" she shouted.
She pulled string number six.
The machine stopped.

14

Ben and Ellie looked at all the mess.

"We're sorry," they said.

But Granny wasn't cross. She had an enormous smile on her face.

"Look!" she said. "There's the kitten."

"Purrrrr," said the cat.

Boom! went the machine.

Questions to ask when the child has read the story

Understanding check:

- What did Granny Gadget lose? Did she find it? How?
- What happened to the housework machine at the end of the story?

Reading skills check:

- Turn to page 8. Ask the child to read this page again. What do you notice about the words on this page? *(some of them rhyme)* Can you find any words that rhyme with each other? *(two/grew, three/bee)*
- Look at page 9. Can you find any rhyming words on this page? *(four/roar, five/alive)*

Focus check: reasons for events

- What happened when the children started the machine for finding lost pets?
- Why did Ben and Ellie get out the housework machine?
- Why wasn't Granny cross at the end of the story?

To develop fluency:

- It is difficult to read a book fluently the first time. Encourage the child to read the book again, paying attention to speech and punctuation, and reading with expression.

Focus

Reasons for events

Granny Gadget

Granny Gadget makes machines to do all kinds of things. But when she loses her kitten, she finds out that her machines don't always work very well . . .

star
GUIDED

GUIDED READING LINK

Jumping Jack

To find out more about Rigby products, plus free supporting resources, visit

www.rigbyed.co.uk
01865 888020

ISBN 978-0-433030-44-7

9 780433 030447

PLAYS
TO READ

Presented by
Julia Donaldson

THE SUMMER EXPLORERS

Written by
Cath Howe

Illustrated by
Roger Simó

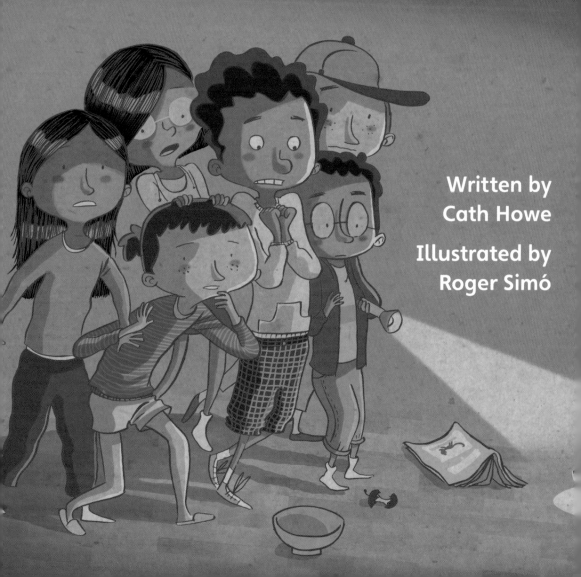

How to handle bats

In one of these plays, the children find a bat flying around their holiday cottage. If you ever find a bat indoors, here's what to do:

- Keep calm, and don't move around too much, so that the bat doesn't become distressed.

- If the bat is trapped in a room, dim the lights. Close the door and open the windows as widely as possible. The bat will eventually find its way out on its own.

- Never try to catch a flying bat – you may hurt it, or it may try to bite or scratch you.

- If you ever do have to handle a bat, wear protective gloves. Although getting bitten or scratched by a bat is rare, if you are bitten wash the wound very carefully and seek medical advice.